Remember Me

by Sally Murphy
illustrated by Roberto Fino

Table of Contents

Across the Sea

September, 1620

My name is Remember Allerton. I am keeping this diary so people will remember me. Our ship is the *Mayflower*. We have left England. We are going across the sea.

October, 1620

I am so sick! There are storms and big waves. My sister Mary and I cuddle with Mother.

November, 1620

We see land! But we cannot leave the boat. There are no homes to live in yet.

A New Camp

December, 1620

We still have to live on the boat. I am so tired of it! Father says I must be patient. The men are building houses.

February, 1621

I wish I was back home in my favorite chair. Our new life is hard.

March, 1621

At last, we have settled in our new house. Today a man named Squanto came. His face was wrinkled. He practiced his English with us. Maybe Squanto can help us.

June, 1621

I have a new friend. Her name is Sanu. She knows all about the plants and animals.

I am learning so much.

Thanksgiving

September, 1621

The crops are growing tall! Soon it will be time to pick them. The leaves are turning colors. It is beautiful here.

October, 1621

We picked all the crops. We worked hard. We have food for winter. Now we can have a big feast. We are so thankful!

Comprehension Check

Retell the Story

Use a Predictions
Chart and the pictures
to help you retell
this story.

What I Predict	What Happens

Think and Compare

1. Turn to page 6. What makes you think the families will soon build homes? *(Make and Confirm Predictions)*

2. What would you enjoy most about moving to a new country? *(Evaluate)*

3. How can people help others to settle in a new home? *(Apply)*